Yogi Just Like Mommy

Written by
Jonelle M. Owens

Illustrated by
F. Parishani

Yogi Just Like Mommy

For information please address
yogijustlikemommy@gmail.com.

First Edition
ISBN: 978-0-578-79573-7

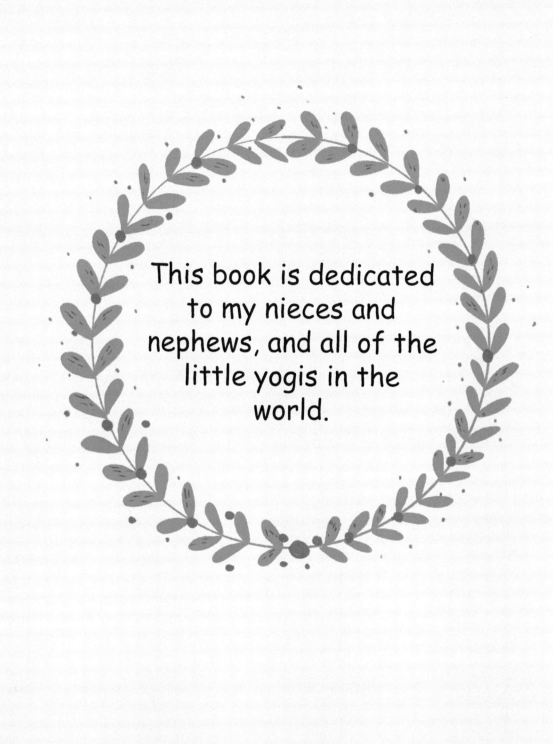

This book is dedicated to my nieces and nephews, and all of the little yogis in the world.

I wake up early in the morning –

Just like Mommy.

Mom gives kisses and hugs
She is so proud of me
And says that I'm a yogi just like Mommy!

Namaste

I wash my face and brush my teeth –
Just like Mommy.

I meet her downstairs
And get ready for today's session.
I meditate.
Shhhh! Silence, no words mentioned –
Just like Mommy.

Now, my feet are planted on the floor.
I do a great biiiiiiig stretch,
Reaching my arms for the ceiling
Looking for sunbeams to catch –
Just like Mommy.

I take a big breath in and a big breath out.
Then it's time to repeat –
A big breath in and let all the air out.
Just a few more beats –
Just like Mommy.

Next, I start the standing tree pose,
my favorite.
Then, I bend and touch my toes
Returning to a deep back stretch
Enjoying the way it flows –
Just like Mommy.

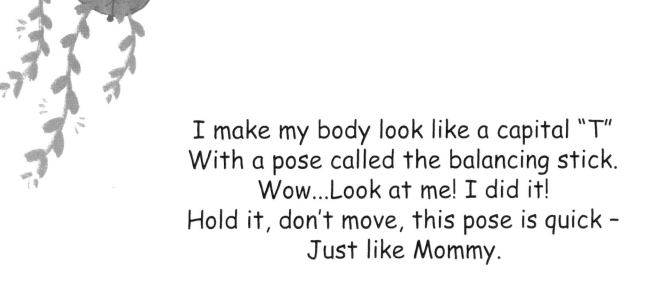

I make my body look like a capital "T"
With a pose called the balancing stick.
Wow...Look at me! I did it!
Hold it, don't move, this pose is quick –
Just like Mommy.

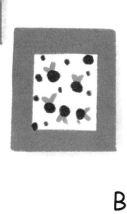

Before lying down and resting,
I finish my standing yoga moves.
These help to get me in the mood
For all my floor yoga grooves –
Just like Mommy

I continue with the wind removing pose.
Knees right up to my chest,
I grab my shin and pull
Giving it my best –
Just like Mommy.

I didn't forget the other leg.
Everything done on one side
I must complete on the other.
Now, I'll do as described –
Just like Mommy.

Next is my other favorite, the bow pose.
I lay on my stomach and grab my feet.
Then pull up my knees and chest.
This pose is really neat –
Just like Mommy.

I breathe in and out
And I never fret.
Soon I will end
After this last set –
Just like Mommy

Just one more pose
Before I'm finished.
Spine twisting pose.
I feel replenished –
Just like Mommy.

I'm all done
And I feel whole.
I am complete
And that was the goal.